THIS BOOK BELONGS TO:

_____

Design by Bee & Moon
Typesetting by Racing Pigeon Productions

Graphics used in this book are derivative of various Creative Commons works (CC0), public domain works, or the creation of the authors. Original source material is from *Manners, Custom and Dress During the Middle Ages and During the Renaissance Period*, by Paul Lacroix (1871); *The Comet of 1618 over Augsburg* by Elias Ehinger (1573-1653]; *L'atmosphère: Météorologie Populaire* by Camille Flammarion (1888); cover images from Adobe Stock.

http://beeandmoon.com

LOVE
IN THE TIME OF
THE PLAGUE

(A Survival Journal and Keepsake)

KATIE MACALISTER

L.K. GLOVER

HOW TO USE THIS JOURNAL

There are almost as many ways to use this book as there are stars in the sky.

You are limited only by your creativity, but just in case you are a bit hesitant to dive right in, let's take a closer look at how the pages are broken down, and meaningful ways you can utilize the sections.

J·F·**M**·A·M·J·J·A·S·O·N·D

4th - 11th
_____ ,

3rd
_____ week of the plague

Weather is crappy. Snow, snow, snow. How much snow could a snow goose snew if a snow goose could snew snow?

Fair winds or foul?

Feeding the huddled masses

Recipe: chicken shawarma **1**

2 *Turkey breast? Need fixings...*

Tacos five times this week. It's self-care. **3**

4 *Make birthday cake for Gidget!*

It was the best of times . . .

Start by noting the week and month, and if you are keeping track, how many days of plague you've survived. You can also track weather for the week, or perhaps make a quick note of something that affected your mood.

If you are artistic, feel free to do a little drawing in the Wreath of Much Artistry, and note down recipes to try, or specific meal plans in the Feeding Huddle Masses section.

The Best of Times allows you to focus on the positive things that are happening in your life...or those you wish would happen. Likewise, the Worst of Times section lets you vent your spleen where only you can see it.

. . . It was the worst of times

People I want to punch in the throat:

Hitler
Emperor Palpatine
Many politicians
Larry from accounting (that little weasel!)
The health insurance dude who hung up on me after I was on hold for forty-three minutes.

My wattle and daub
(And I don't mean my second chin)

Hiked up Bridal Trail Falls in the am.
Dogs loved it, especially when we reached
the falls themselves. There was a herd of
wild bunnies frolicking around. It was
gloriously fabulous, in a Disney sort of way.
Got some great pictures of Nicky and the
bun-buns.

Four spots are provided in Drawn and Quartered for
you to pen a (very small) epic poem, draw something
that caught your eye, compose an (also very small) ode,
map out the way through the pandemic. etc.

The hedge witch inspired me to draw this

Found this card in an old
book. So pretty!

Drawn AND Quartered

Don't throw me on the cart . . .

watercolor goals!

. . . I'm just having a Monday

The world according to me

Backyard picnic ideas:

Ben's barbeque chicken
red, white, and blue potato salad
five bags of chips (because there is no
such thing as too many picnic chips)
stuffed celery
grany smith salad
grapes, grapes, grapes!
watermelon cooler?

	The rash is gone!	Slightly flushed	A few pustules	Throw me on the cart
S	●	○	○	○
M	●	○	○	○
T	○	○	●	○
W	○	○	○	●
T	○	●	○	○
F	○	●	○	○
S	●	○	○	○

Ball~pit of my mind
(dump whatever you want in this space; just wash your hands afterward)

Since the authors are both big fans of checklists (is there anything so satisfying as checking off things?) you have a big space to make a to-do list of everything needed to be done during the week.

Because your emotional and mental health is important in this time of plague, you have a way to track how you're feeling each day of the week. The Ball Pit gives you a way to dump thoughts that won't go away, and the Habit Tracker...well, tracks habits.

Habit check~in

S	M	T	W	T	F	S
○	○	○	○	○	○	○
○	●	●	○	○	○	○
●	○	○	●	●	●	○
●	●	○	○	●	●	●
○	●	○	●	○	○	●
●	●	○	●	○	●	●
○	○	○	○	○	○	○

(Did you do your stuff?)

Work on poem
Cook dinner five times this week.
Doodle a day
Work on taxes
Don't murder anyone

The last page in each week's set has two focuses: the first is a fun image you can color (please test markers and pens on a back page before using in the main part of the journal), and the second is divided space available for reflection, prayers, more notes on things to be done (can you ever have enough space for that?), and a hundred other things.

You can even use the space to make lists of all the things you can put on those pages! The choice is up to you.

Aligning my humours . . .

AND
NOW . . .

THE
WEEKLY
PAGES

J·F·M·A·M·J·J·A·S·O·N·D

_____,

_____ week of the plague

Fair winds or foul?

It was the best of times . . .

. . . It was the worst of times

Feeding the huddled masses

1

2

3

4

My wattle and daub
(And I don't mean my second chin)

The hedge witch inspired
me to draw this

Drawn
AND
Quartered

Don't throw me
on the cart . . .

The world
according to me

. . . I'm just having a Monday

the pustules burst:

- [ ]
- [ ]
- [ ]
- [ ]
- [ ]
- [ ]
- [ ]
- [ ]
- [ ]
- [ ]
- [ ]
- [ ]
- [ ]
- [ ]
- [ ]
- [ ]
- [ ]
- [ ]
- [ ]

(How is your plague?)

	The rash is gone!	Slightly flushed	A few pustules	Throw me on the cart
S	○	○	○	○
M	○	○	○	○
T	○	○	○	○
W	○	○	○	○
T	○	○	○	○
F	○	○	○	○
S	○	○	○	○

Ball~pit of my mind
(dump whatever you want in this space; just wash your hands afterward)

Habit check~in

S	M	T	W	T	F	S
○	○	○	○	○	○	○
○	○	○	○	○	○	○
○	○	○	○	○	○	○
○	○	○	○	○	○	○
○	○	○	○	○	○	○
○	○	○	○	○	○	○
○	○	○	○	○	○	○

(Did you do your stuff?)

Aligning my humours . . .

J·F·M·A·M·J·J·A·S·O·N·D

_____ ,

_____ week of the plague

Fair winds or foul?

Feeding the huddled masses

1

2

3

4

It was the best of times . . .

. . . It was the worst of times

My wattle and daub
(And I don't mean my second chin)

The hedge witch inspired
me to draw this

Don't throw me
on the cart . . .

Drawn AND Quartered

The world
according to me

. . . I'm just having a Monday

	The rash is gone!	Slightly flushed	A few pustules	Throw me on the cart
S	○	○	○	○
M	○	○	○	○
T	○	○	○	○
W	○	○	○	○
T	○	○	○	○
F	○	○	○	○
S	○	○	○	○

Ball~pit of my mind
(dump whatever you want in this space; just wash your hands afterward)

Habit check~in

S	M	T	W	T	F	S
○	○	○	○	○	○	○
○	○	○	○	○	○	○
○	○	○	○	○	○	○
○	○	○	○	○	○	○
○	○	○	○	○	○	○
○	○	○	○	○	○	○
○	○	○	○	○	○	○

(Did you do your stuff?)

It's written in the stars.

J·F·M·A·M·J·J·A·S·O·N·D

_____,

_____ week of the plague

Fair winds or foul?

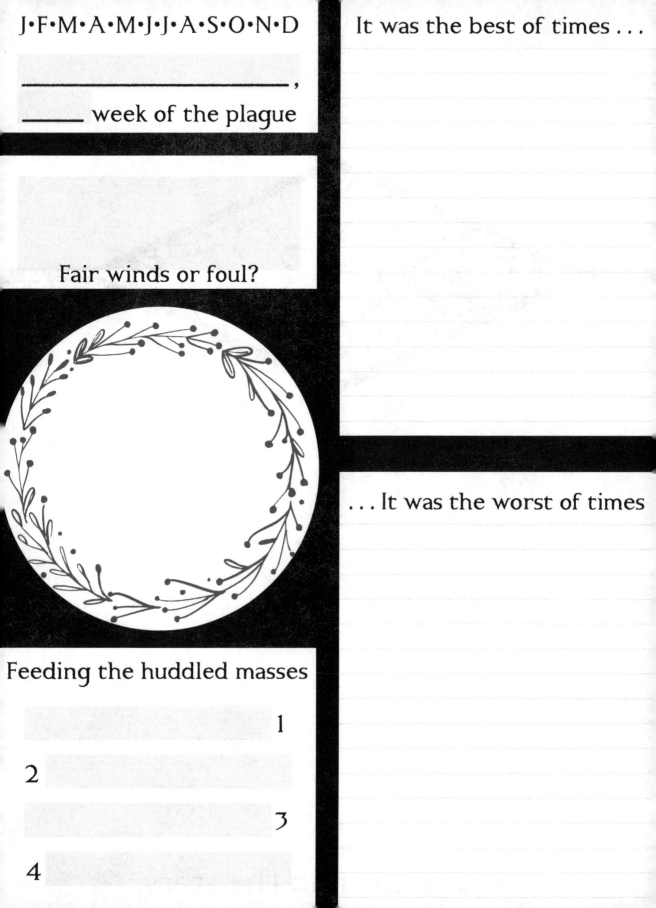

It was the best of times . . .

. . . It was the worst of times

Feeding the huddled masses

1

2

3

4

My wattle and daub
(And I don't mean my second chin)

The hedge witch inspired
me to draw this

Drawn
AND
Quartered

Don't throw me
on the cart . . .

The world
according to me

. . . I'm just having a Monday

Stuff to do before the pustules burst:

- [ ]
- [ ]
- [ ]
- [ ]
- [ ]
- [ ]
- [ ]
- [ ]
- [ ]
- [ ]
- [ ]
- [ ]
- [ ]
- [ ]
- [ ]
- [ ]
- [ ]
- [ ]
- [ ]

Emotional check~in
(How is your plague?)

	The rash is gone!	Slightly flushed	A few pustules	Throw me on the cart
S	○	○	○	○
M	○	○	○	○
T	○	○	○	○
W	○	○	○	○
T	○	○	○	○
F	○	○	○	○
S	○	○	○	○

Ball~pit of my mind
(dump whatever you want in this space; just wash your hands afterward)

Habit check~in

S	M	T	W	T	F	S
○	○	○	○	○	○	○
○	○	○	○	○	○	○
○	○	○	○	○	○	○
○	○	○	○	○	○	○
○	○	○	○	○	○	○
○	○	○	○	○	○	○
○	○	○	○	○	○	○

(Did you do your stuff?)

Love in the time of the plague.

J·F·M·A·M·J·J·A·S·O·N·D

_____ ,

_____ week of the plague

Fair winds or foul?

Feeding the huddled masses

1

2

3

4

It was the best of times . . .

. . . It was the worst of times

My wattle and daub
(And I don't mean my second chin)

The hedge witch inspired
me to draw this

Drawn
AND
Quartered

Don't throw me
on the cart . . .

The world
according to me

. . . I'm just having a Monday

Stuff to do before the pustules burst:

- [ ]
- [ ]
- [ ]
- [ ]
- [ ]
- [ ]
- [ ]
- [ ]
- [ ]
- [ ]
- [ ]
- [ ]
- [ ]
- [ ]
- [ ]
- [ ]
- [ ]

Emotional check~in
(How is your plague?)

	The rash is gone!	Slightly flushed	A few pustules	Throw me on the cart
S	◯	◯	◯	◯
M	◯	◯	◯	◯
T	◯	◯	◯	◯
W	◯	◯	◯	◯
T	◯	◯	◯	◯
F	◯	◯	◯	◯
S	◯	◯	◯	◯

Ball~pit of my mind
(dump whatever you want in this space; just wash your hands afterward)

Habit check~in

S	M	T	W	T	F	S
◯	◯	◯	◯	◯	◯	◯
◯	◯	◯	◯	◯	◯	◯
◯	◯	◯	◯	◯	◯	◯
◯	◯	◯	◯	◯	◯	◯
◯	◯	◯	◯	◯	◯	◯
◯	◯	◯	◯	◯	◯	◯
◯	◯	◯	◯	◯	◯	◯

(Did you do your stuff?)

Turning lead into gold.

J·F·M·A·M·J·J·A·S·O·N·D

———————————————————,

_____ week of the plague

Fair winds or foul?

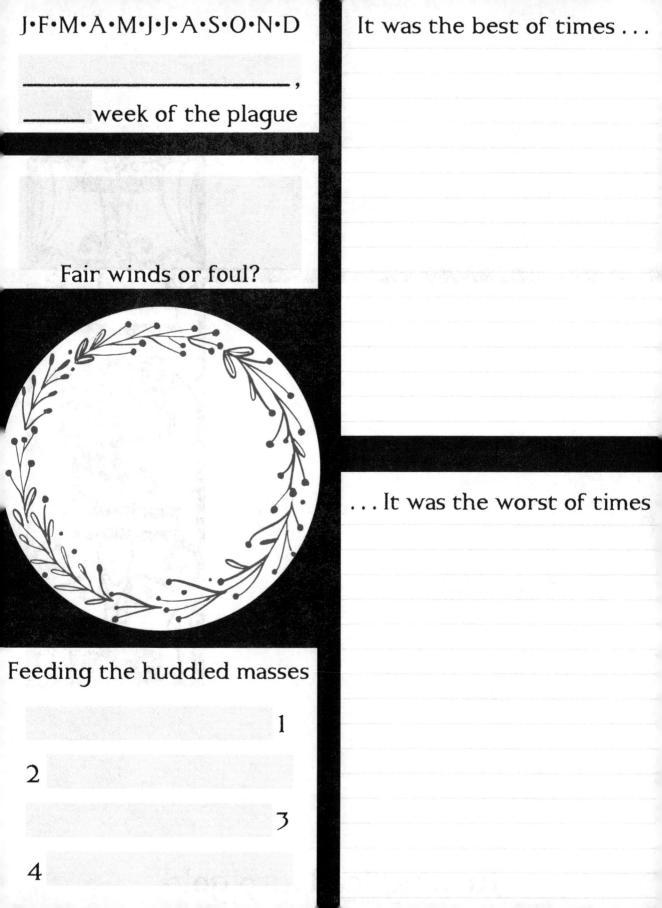

It was the best of times . . .

. . . It was the worst of times

Feeding the huddled masses

1

2

3

4

My wattle and daub
(And I don't mean my second chin)

The hedge witch inspired
me to draw this

Drawn
AND
Quartered

Don't throw me
on the cart . . .

The world
according to me

. . . I'm just having a Monday

Stuff to do before the pustules burst:

☐ ....
☐ ....
☐ ....
☐ ....
☐ ....
☐ ....
☐ ....
☐ ....
☐ ....
☐ ....
☐ ....
☐ ....
☐ ....
☐ ....
☐ ....
☐ ....

Emotional check~in
(How is your plague?)

	The rash is gone!	Slightly flushed	A few pustules	Throw me on the cart
S	○	○	○	○
M	○	○	○	○
T	○	○	○	○
W	○	○	○	○
T	○	○	○	○
F	○	○	○	○
S	○	○	○	○

Ball~pit of my mind
(dump whatever you want in this space; just wash your hands afterward)

Habit check~in

S	M	T	W	T	F	S
○	○	○	○	○	○	○
○	○	○	○	○	○	○
○	○	○	○	○	○	○
○	○	○	○	○	○	○
○	○	○	○	○	○	○
○	○	○	○	○	○	○
○	○	○	○	○	○	○

(Did you do your stuff?)

Today, fate is being . . .

J·F·M·A·M·J·J·A·S·O·N·D

_____,

_____ week of the plague

Fair winds or foul?

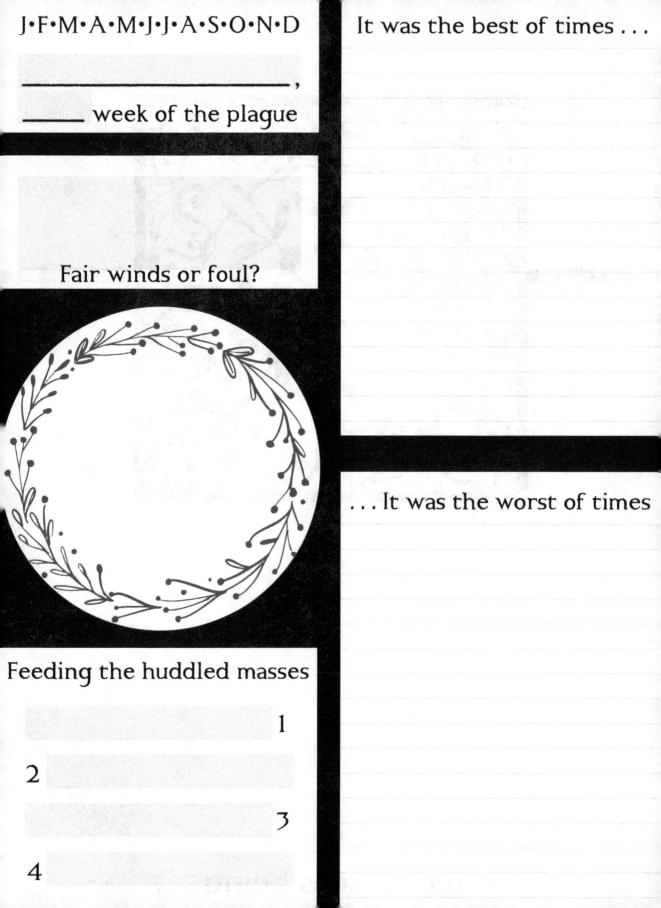

Feeding the huddled masses

1

2

3

4

It was the best of times . . .

. . . It was the worst of times

My wattle and daub
(And I don't mean my second chin)

The hedge witch inspired
me to draw this

Drawn
AND
Quartered

Don't throw me
on the cart . . .

The world
according to me

. . . I'm just having a Monday

Stuff to do before the pustules burst:

- [ ]
- [ ]
- [ ]
- [ ]
- [ ]
- [ ]
- [ ]
- [ ]
- [ ]
- [ ]
- [ ]
- [ ]
- [ ]
- [ ]
- [ ]
- [ ]
- [ ]
- [ ]
- [ ]

Emotional check~in
(How is your plague?)

	The rash is gone!	Slightly flushed	A few pustules	Throw me on the cart
S	○	○	○	○
M	○	○	○	○
T	○	○	○	○
W	○	○	○	○
T	○	○	○	○
F	○	○	○	○
S	○	○	○	○

Ball~pit of my mind
(dump whatever you want in this space; just wash your hands afterward)

Habit check~in

S	M	T	W	T	F	S
○	○	○	○	○	○	○
○	○	○	○	○	○	○
○	○	○	○	○	○	○
○	○	○	○	○	○	○
○	○	○	○	○	○	○
○	○	○	○	○	○	○
○	○	○	○	○	○	○

(Did you do your stuff?)

The Oracle says . . .

J·F·M·A·M·J·J·A·S·O·N·D

_____,

_____ week of the plague

Fair winds or foul?

It was the best of times . . .

. . . It was the worst of times

Feeding the huddled masses

1

2

3

4

My wattle and daub
(And I don't mean my second chin)

The hedge witch inspired
me to draw this

Don't throw me
on the cart . . .

The world
according to me

. . . I'm just having a Monday

Stuff to do before the pustules burst:

- [ ]
- [ ]
- [ ]
- [ ]
- [ ]
- [ ]
- [ ]
- [ ]
- [ ]
- [ ]
- [ ]
- [ ]
- [ ]
- [ ]
- [ ]
- [ ]
- [ ]

Emotional check~in
(How is your plague?)

	The rash is gone!	Slightly flushed	A few pustules	Throw me on the cart
S	○	○	○	○
M	○	○	○	○
T	○	○	○	○
W	○	○	○	○
T	○	○	○	○
F	○	○	○	○
S	○	○	○	○

Ball~pit of my mind
(dump whatever you want in this space; just wash your hands afterward)

Habit check~in

S	M	T	W	T	F	S
○	○	○	○	○	○	○
○	○	○	○	○	○	○
○	○	○	○	○	○	○
○	○	○	○	○	○	○
○	○	○	○	○	○	○
○	○	○	○	○	○	○
○	○	○	○	○	○	○

(Did you do your stuff?)

Aligning my humours . . .

J·F·M·A·M·J·J·A·S·O·N·D

_____,

_____ week of the plague

Fair winds or foul?

It was the best of times . . .

. . . It was the worst of times

Feeding the huddled masses

1

2

3

4

My wattle and daub
(And I don't mean my second chin)

The hedge witch inspired
me to draw this

Drawn AND Quartered

Don't throw me
on the cart . . .

The world
according to me

. . . I'm just having a Monday

	The rash is gone!	Slightly flushed	A few pustules	Throw me on the cart
S	○	○	○	○
M	○	○	○	○
T	○	○	○	○
W	○	○	○	○
T	○	○	○	○
F	○	○	○	○
S	○	○	○	○

Ball~pit of my mind
(dump whatever you want in this space; just wash your hands afterward)

Habit check~in

S	M	T	W	T	F	S
○	○	○	○	○	○	○
○	○	○	○	○	○	○
○	○	○	○	○	○	○
○	○	○	○	○	○	○
○	○	○	○	○	○	○
○	○	○	○	○	○	○
○	○	○	○	○	○	○

(Did you do your stuff?)

It's written in the stars.

J·F·M·A·M·J·J·A·S·O·N·D

_____,

_____ week of the plague

Fair winds or foul?

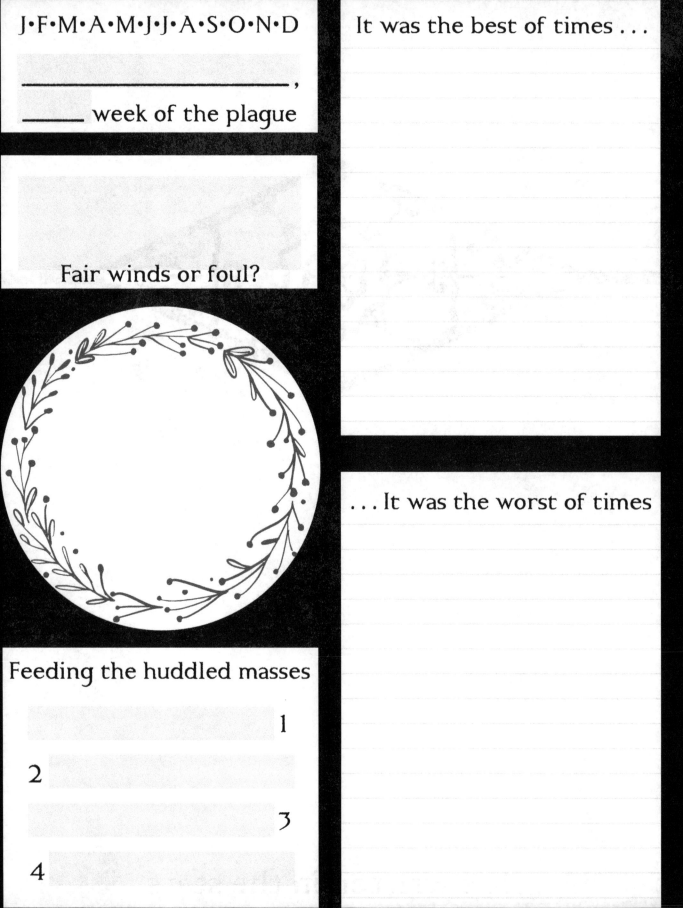

Feeding the huddled masses

1

2

3

4

It was the best of times . . .

. . . It was the worst of times

My wattle and daub
(And I don't mean my second chin)

The hedge witch inspired
me to draw this

Drawn
AND
Quartered

Don't throw me
on the cart . . .

The world
according to me

. . . I'm just having a Monday

Stuff to do before the pustules burst:

- [ ]
- [ ]
- [ ]
- [ ]
- [ ]
- [ ]
- [ ]
- [ ]
- [ ]
- [ ]
- [ ]
- [ ]
- [ ]
- [ ]
- [ ]
- [ ]

Emotional check~in
(How is your plague?)

	The rash is gone!	Slightly flushed	A few pustules	Throw me on the cart
S	○	○	○	○
M	○	○	○	○
T	○	○	○	○
W	○	○	○	○
T	○	○	○	○
F	○	○	○	○
S	○	○	○	○

Ball~pit of my mind
(dump whatever you want in this space; just wash your hands afterward)

Habit check~in

S	M	T	W	T	F	S
○	○	○	○	○	○	○
○	○	○	○	○	○	○
○	○	○	○	○	○	○
○	○	○	○	○	○	○
○	○	○	○	○	○	○
○	○	○	○	○	○	○
○	○	○	○	○	○	○

(Did you do your stuff?)

Love in the time of the plague.

J·F·M·A·M·J·J·A·S·O·N·D

_____,

_____ week of the plague

Fair winds or foul?

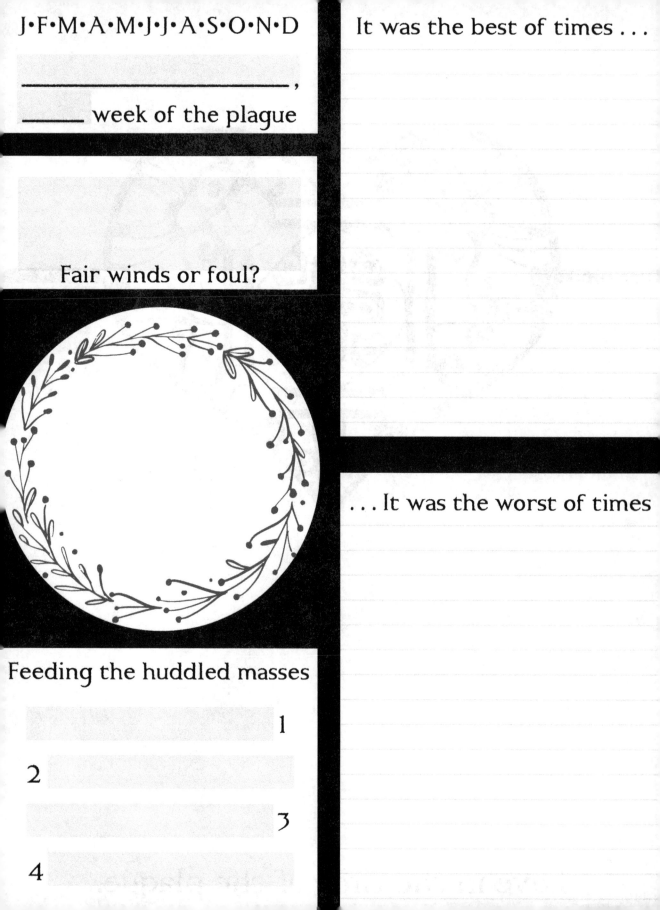

It was the best of times . . .

. . . It was the worst of times

Feeding the huddled masses

1

2

3

4

My wattle and daub
(And I don't mean my second chin)

The hedge witch inspired
me to draw this

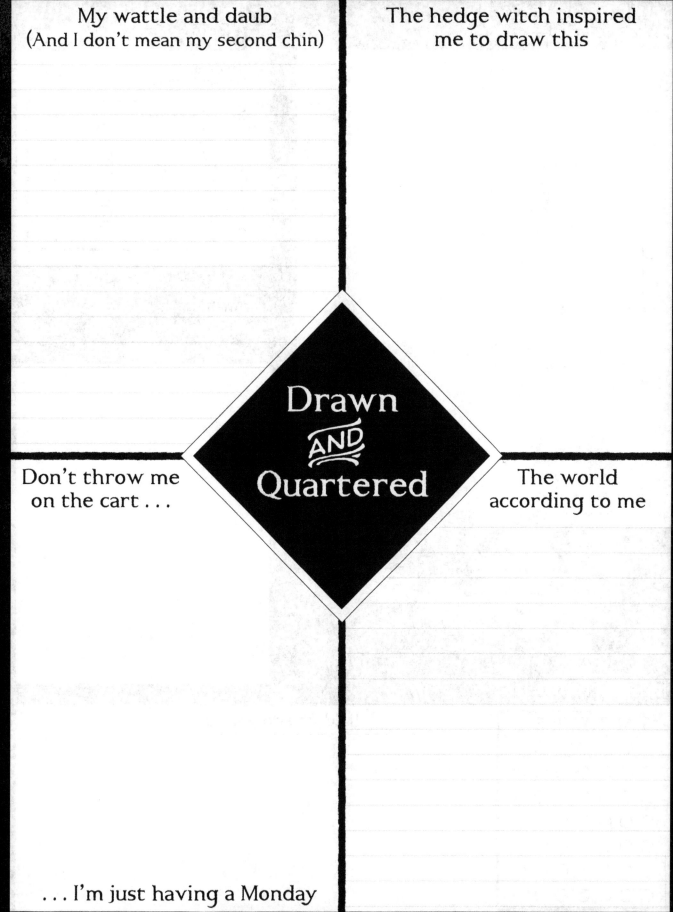

Drawn
AND
Quartered

Don't throw me
on the cart . . .

The world
according to me

. . . I'm just having a Monday

Stuff to do before the pustules burst:

- [ ]
- [ ]
- [ ]
- [ ]
- [ ]
- [ ]
- [ ]
- [ ]
- [ ]
- [ ]
- [ ]
- [ ]
- [ ]
- [ ]
- [ ]
- [ ]
- [ ]

Emotional check~in
(How is your plague?)

	The rash is gone!	Slightly flushed	A few pustules	Throw me on the cart
S	○	○	○	○
M	○	○	○	○
T	○	○	○	○
W	○	○	○	○
T	○	○	○	○
F	○	○	○	○
S	○	○	○	○

Ball~pit of my mind
(dump whatever you want in this space; just wash your hands afterward)

Habit check~in

S	M	T	W	T	F	S
○	○	○	○	○	○	○
○	○	○	○	○	○	○
○	○	○	○	○	○	○
○	○	○	○	○	○	○
○	○	○	○	○	○	○
○	○	○	○	○	○	○
○	○	○	○	○	○	○

(Did you do your stuff?)

Turning lead into gold.

J·F·M·A·M·J·J·A·S·O·N·D

_____,

_____ week of the plague

Fair winds or foul?

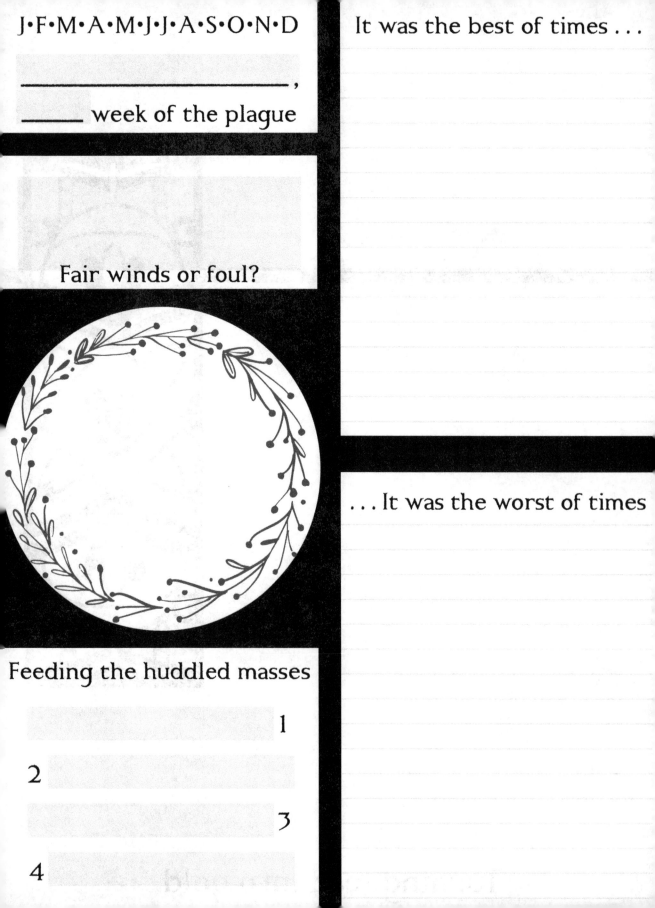

Feeding the huddled masses

1

2

3

4

It was the best of times . . .

. . . It was the worst of times

My wattle and daub
(And I don't mean my second chin)

The hedge witch inspired
me to draw this

Drawn AND Quartered

Don't throw me
on the cart . . .

The world
according to me

. . . I'm just having a Monday

	The rash is gone!	Slightly flushed	A few pustules	Throw me on the cart
S	○	○	○	○
M	○	○	○	○
T	○	○	○	○
W	○	○	○	○
T	○	○	○	○
F	○	○	○	○
S	○	○	○	○

Ball~pit of my mind
(dump whatever you want in this space; just wash your hands afterward)

Habit check~in

S	M	T	W	T	F	S
○	○	○	○	○	○	○
○	○	○	○	○	○	○
○	○	○	○	○	○	○
○	○	○	○	○	○	○
○	○	○	○	○	○	○
○	○	○	○	○	○	○
○	○	○	○	○	○	○

(Did you do your stuff?)

Today, fate is being . . .

J·F·M·A·M·J·J·A·S·O·N·D

_____ ,

_____ week of the plague

Fair winds or foul?

Feeding the huddled masses

	1
2	
	3
4	

It was the best of times . . .

. . . It was the worst of times

My wattle and daub
(And I don't mean my second chin)

The hedge witch inspired
me to draw this

Drawn
AND
Quartered

Don't throw me
on the cart . . .

The world
according to me

. . . I'm just having a Monday

the pustules burst:

- [ ]
- [ ]
- [ ]
- [ ]
- [ ]
- [ ]
- [ ]
- [ ]
- [ ]
- [ ]
- [ ]
- [ ]
- [ ]
- [ ]
- [ ]
- [ ]
- [ ]
- [ ]
- [ ]

(How is your plague?)

	The rash is gone!	Slightly flushed	A few pustules	Throw me on the cart
S	○	○	○	○
M	○	○	○	○
T	○	○	○	○
W	○	○	○	○
T	○	○	○	○
F	○	○	○	○
S	○	○	○	○

Ball~pit of my mind
(dump whatever you want in this space; just wash your hands afterward)

Habit check~in

S	M	T	W	T	F	S
○	○	○	○	○	○	○
○	○	○	○	○	○	○
○	○	○	○	○	○	○
○	○	○	○	○	○	○
○	○	○	○	○	○	○
○	○	○	○	○	○	○
○	○	○	○	○	○	○

(Did you do your stuff?)

The Oracle says . . .

J·F·M·A·M·J·J·A·S·O·N·D

_____ ,

_____ week of the plague

Fair winds or foul?

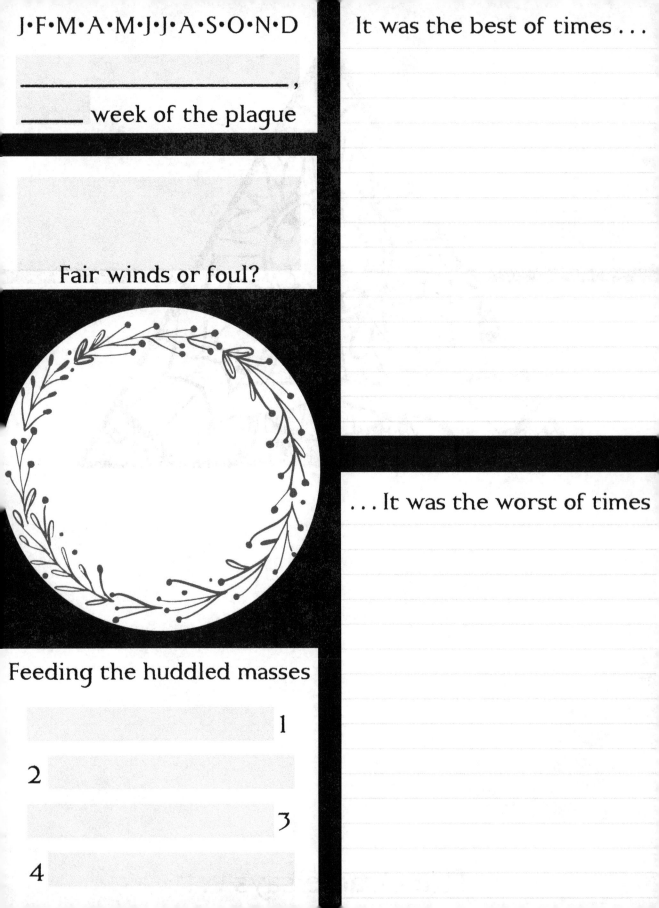

It was the best of times . . .

. . . It was the worst of times

Feeding the huddled masses

1

2

3

4

My wattle and daub
(And I don't mean my second chin)

The hedge witch inspired
me to draw this

Don't throw me
on the cart . . .

Drawn
AND
Quartered

The world
according to me

. . . I'm just having a Monday

the pustules burst:

	The rash is gone!	Slightly flushed	A few pustules	Throw me on the cart
S	◯	◯	◯	◯
M	◯	◯	◯	◯
T	◯	◯	◯	◯
W	◯	◯	◯	◯
T	◯	◯	◯	◯
F	◯	◯	◯	◯
S	◯	◯	◯	◯

Ball~pit of my mind
(dump whatever you want in this space; just wash your hands afterward)

Habit check~in

S	M	T	W	T	F	S
◯	◯	◯	◯	◯	◯	◯
◯	◯	◯	◯	◯	◯	◯
◯	◯	◯	◯	◯	◯	◯
◯	◯	◯	◯	◯	◯	◯
◯	◯	◯	◯	◯	◯	◯
◯	◯	◯	◯	◯	◯	◯
◯	◯	◯	◯	◯	◯	◯

(Did you do your stuff?)

Aligning my humours . . .

J·F·M·A·M·J·J·A·S·O·N·D

_____ ,

_____ week of the plague

Fair winds or foul?

Feeding the huddled masses

1

2

3

4

It was the best of times . . .

. . . It was the worst of times

My wattle and daub
(And I don't mean my second chin)

The hedge witch inspired
me to draw this

Don't throw me
on the cart . . .

Drawn
AND
Quartered

The world
according to me

. . . I'm just having a Monday

the pustules burst:

	The rash is gone!	Slightly flushed	A few pustules	Throw me on the cart
S	○	○	○	○
M	○	○	○	○
T	○	○	○	○
W	○	○	○	○
T	○	○	○	○
F	○	○	○	○
S	○	○	○	○

Ball~pit of my mind
(dump whatever you want in this space; just wash your hands afterward)

Habit check~in

S	M	T	W	T	F	S
○	○	○	○	○	○	○
○	○	○	○	○	○	○
○	○	○	○	○	○	○
○	○	○	○	○	○	○
○	○	○	○	○	○	○
○	○	○	○	○	○	○
○	○	○	○	○	○	○

(Did you do your stuff?)

It's written in the stars.

J·F·M·A·M·J·J·A·S·O·N·D

_____,

_____ week of the plague

Fair winds or foul?

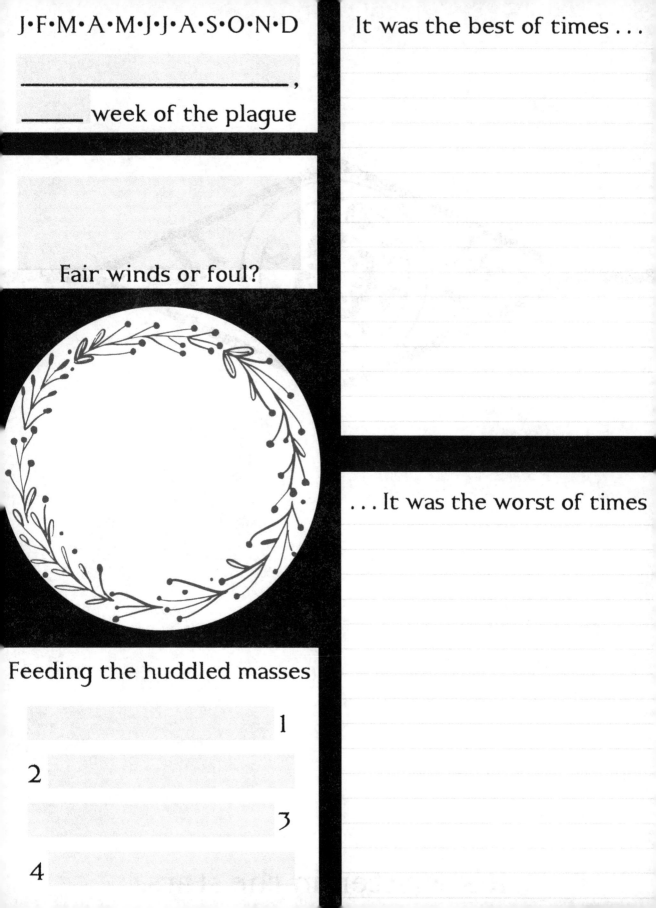

Feeding the huddled masses

1

2

3

4

It was the best of times . . .

. . . It was the worst of times

My wattle and daub
(And I don't mean my second chin)

The hedge witch inspired
me to draw this

Drawn
AND
Quartered

Don't throw me
on the cart . . .

The world
according to me

. . . I'm just having a Monday

Stuff to do before the pustules burst:

- ☐
- ☐
- ☐
- ☐
- ☐
- ☐
- ☐
- ☐
- ☐
- ☐
- ☐
- ☐
- ☐
- ☐
- ☐
- ☐
- ☐
- ☐

Emotional check~in
(How is your plague?)

	The rash is gone!	Slightly flushed	A few pustules	Throw me on the cart
S	○	○	○	○
M	○	○	○	○
T	○	○	○	○
W	○	○	○	○
T	○	○	○	○
F	○	○	○	○
S	○	○	○	○

Ball~pit of my mind
(dump whatever you want in this space; just wash your hands afterward)

Habit check~in

S	M	T	W	T	F	S
○	○	○	○	○	○	○
○	○	○	○	○	○	○
○	○	○	○	○	○	○
○	○	○	○	○	○	○
○	○	○	○	○	○	○
○	○	○	○	○	○	○
○	○	○	○	○	○	○

(Did you do your stuff?)

Love in the time of the plague.

J·F·M·A·M·J·J·A·S·O·N·D

_____ ,

_____ week of the plague

Fair winds or foul?

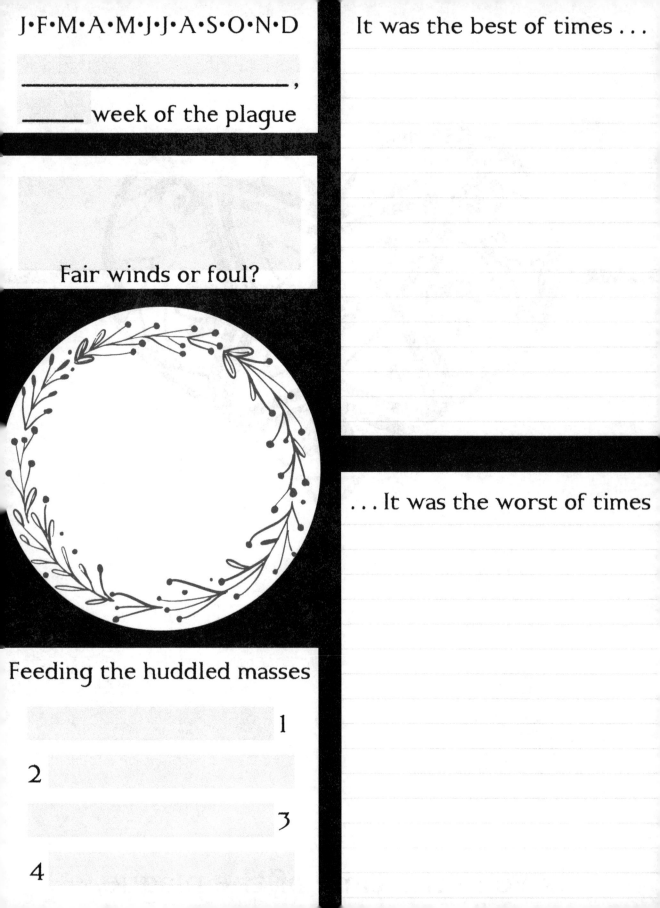

Feeding the huddled masses

1

2

3

4

It was the best of times . . .

. . . It was the worst of times

My wattle and daub
(And I don't mean my second chin)

The hedge witch inspired
me to draw this

Drawn
AND
Quartered

Don't throw me
on the cart . . .

The world
according to me

. . . I'm just having a Monday

the pustules burst:

	The rash is gone!	Slightly flushed	A few pustules	Throw me on the cart
S	○	○	○	○
M	○	○	○	○
T	○	○	○	○
W	○	○	○	○
T	○	○	○	○
F	○	○	○	○
S	○	○	○	○

Ball~pit of my mind
(dump whatever you want in this space; just wash your hands afterward)

Habit check~in

S	M	T	W	T	F	S
○	○	○	○	○	○	○
○	○	○	○	○	○	○
○	○	○	○	○	○	○
○	○	○	○	○	○	○
○	○	○	○	○	○	○
○	○	○	○	○	○	○
○	○	○	○	○	○	○

(Did you do your stuff?)

Turning lead into gold.

J·F·M·A·M·J·J·A·S·O·N·D

It was the best of times . . .

_____,

_____ week of the plague

Fair winds or foul?

. . . It was the worst of times

Feeding the huddled masses

1

2

3

4

My wattle and daub
(And I don't mean my second chin)

The hedge witch inspired
me to draw this

Don't throw me
on the cart . . .

Drawn
AND
Quartered

The world
according to me

. . . I'm just having a Monday

the pustules burst:

- [ ]
- [ ]
- [ ]
- [ ]
- [ ]
- [ ]
- [ ]
- [ ]
- [ ]
- [ ]
- [ ]
- [ ]
- [ ]
- [ ]
- [ ]
- [ ]

(How is your plague?)

	The rash is gone!	Slightly flushed	A few pustules	Throw me on the cart
S	○	○	○	○
M	○	○	○	○
T	○	○	○	○
W	○	○	○	○
T	○	○	○	○
F	○	○	○	○
S	○	○	○	○

Ball~pit of my mind
(dump whatever you want in this space; just wash your hands afterward)

Habit check~in

S	M	T	W	T	F	S
○	○	○	○	○	○	○
○	○	○	○	○	○	○
○	○	○	○	○	○	○
○	○	○	○	○	○	○
○	○	○	○	○	○	○
○	○	○	○	○	○	○
○	○	○	○	○	○	○

(Did you do your stuff?)

Today, fate is being . . .

J·F·M·A·M·J·J·A·S·O·N·D

———————————————,

_____ week of the plague

Fair winds or foul?

It was the best of times . . .

. . . It was the worst of times

Feeding the huddled masses

1

2

3

4

Stuff to do before the pustules burst:

- [ ]
- [ ]
- [ ]
- [ ]
- [ ]
- [ ]
- [ ]
- [ ]
- [ ]
- [ ]
- [ ]
- [ ]
- [ ]
- [ ]
- [ ]
- [ ]

Emotional check~in
(How is your plague?)

	The rash is gone!	Slightly flushed	A few pustules	Throw me on the cart
S	◯	◯	◯	◯
M	◯	◯	◯	◯
T	◯	◯	◯	◯
W	◯	◯	◯	◯
T	◯	◯	◯	◯
F	◯	◯	◯	◯
S	◯	◯	◯	◯

Ball~pit of my mind
(dump whatever you want in this space; just wash your hands afterward)

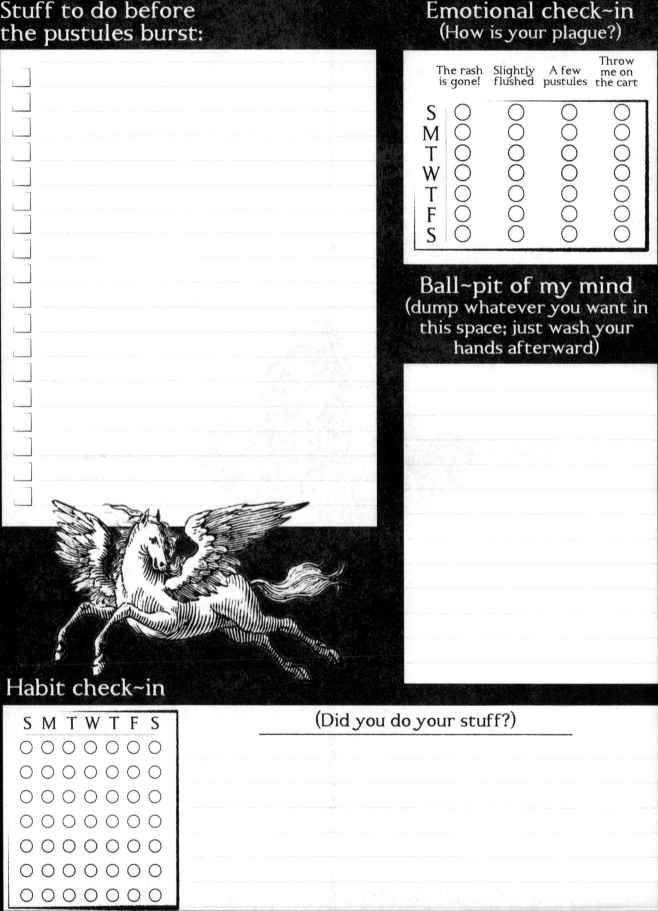

Habit check~in

S	M	T	W	T	F	S
◯	◯	◯	◯	◯	◯	◯
◯	◯	◯	◯	◯	◯	◯
◯	◯	◯	◯	◯	◯	◯
◯	◯	◯	◯	◯	◯	◯
◯	◯	◯	◯	◯	◯	◯
◯	◯	◯	◯	◯	◯	◯
◯	◯	◯	◯	◯	◯	◯

(Did you do your stuff?)

The Oracle says . . .

J·F·M·A·M·J·J·A·S·O·N·D

———————————————————— ,

———— week of the plague

Fair winds or foul?

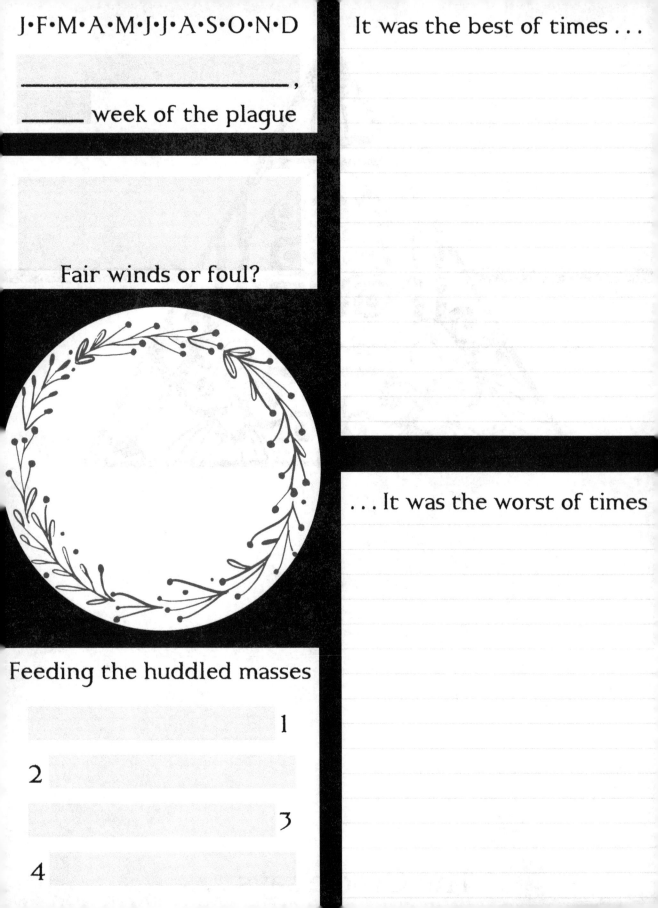

It was the best of times . . .

. . . It was the worst of times

Feeding the huddled masses

1

2

3

4

My wattle and daub
(And I don't mean my second chin)

The hedge witch inspired
me to draw this

Don't throw me
on the cart . . .

Drawn
AND
Quartered

The world
according to me

. . . I'm just having a Monday

Stuff to do before the pustules burst:

- [ ]
- [ ]
- [ ]
- [ ]
- [ ]
- [ ]
- [ ]
- [ ]
- [ ]
- [ ]
- [ ]
- [ ]
- [ ]
- [ ]
- [ ]
- [ ]
- [ ]
- [ ]

Emotional check~in
(How is your plague?)

	The rash is gone!	Slightly flushed	A few pustules	Throw me on the cart
S	○	○	○	○
M	○	○	○	○
T	○	○	○	○
W	○	○	○	○
T	○	○	○	○
F	○	○	○	○
S	○	○	○	○

Ball~pit of my mind
(dump whatever you want in this space; just wash your hands afterward)

Habit check~in

S	M	T	W	T	F	S
○	○	○	○	○	○	○
○	○	○	○	○	○	○
○	○	○	○	○	○	○
○	○	○	○	○	○	○
○	○	○	○	○	○	○
○	○	○	○	○	○	○
○	○	○	○	○	○	○

(Did you do your stuff?)

Aligning my humours . . .

J·F·M·A·M·J·J·A·S·O·N·D

_____ ,

_____ week of the plague

Fair winds or foul?

Feeding the huddled masses

1

2

3

4

It was the best of times . . .

. . . It was the worst of times

My wattle and daub
(And I don't mean my second chin)

The hedge witch inspired
me to draw this

Drawn
AND
Quartered

Don't throw me
on the cart . . .

The world
according to me

. . . I'm just having a Monday

Stuff to do before the pustules burst:

- [ ]
- [ ]
- [ ]
- [ ]
- [ ]
- [ ]
- [ ]
- [ ]
- [ ]
- [ ]
- [ ]
- [ ]
- [ ]
- [ ]
- [ ]
- [ ]
- [ ]
- [ ]

Emotional check~in
(How is your plague?)

	The rash is gone!	Slightly flushed	A few pustules	Throw me on the cart
S	○	○	○	○
M	○	○	○	○
T	○	○	○	○
W	○	○	○	○
T	○	○	○	○
F	○	○	○	○
S	○	○	○	○

Ball~pit of my mind
(dump whatever you want in this space; just wash your hands afterward)

Habit check~in

S	M	T	W	T	F	S
○	○	○	○	○	○	○
○	○	○	○	○	○	○
○	○	○	○	○	○	○
○	○	○	○	○	○	○
○	○	○	○	○	○	○
○	○	○	○	○	○	○
○	○	○	○	○	○	○

(Did you do your stuff?)

It's written in the stars.

J·F·M·A·M·J·J·A·S·O·N·D

_____ ,

_____ week of the plague

Fair winds or foul?

Feeding the huddled masses

1

2

3

4

It was the best of times . . .

. . . It was the worst of times

My wattle and daub
(And I don't mean my second chin)

The hedge witch inspired
me to draw this

Drawn AND Quartered

Don't throw me
on the cart . . .

The world
according to me

. . . I'm just having a Monday

Stuff to do before the pustules burst:

- [ ]
- [ ]
- [ ]
- [ ]
- [ ]
- [ ]
- [ ]
- [ ]
- [ ]
- [ ]
- [ ]
- [ ]
- [ ]
- [ ]
- [ ]
- [ ]
- [ ]
- [ ]
- [ ]
- [ ]

Emotional check~in
(How is your plague?)

	The rash is gone!	Slightly flushed	A few pustules	Throw me on the cart
S	○	○	○	○
M	○	○	○	○
T	○	○	○	○
W	○	○	○	○
T	○	○	○	○
F	○	○	○	○
S	○	○	○	○

Ball~pit of my mind
(dump whatever you want in this space; just wash your hands afterward)

Habit check~in

S	M	T	W	T	F	S
○	○	○	○	○	○	○
○	○	○	○	○	○	○
○	○	○	○	○	○	○
○	○	○	○	○	○	○
○	○	○	○	○	○	○
○	○	○	○	○	○	○
○	○	○	○	○	○	○

(Did you do your stuff?)

Love in the time of the plague.

J·F·M·A·M·J·J·A·S·O·N·D

_____,

_____ week of the plague

Fair winds or foul?

Feeding the huddled masses

1

2

3

4

It was the best of times . . .

. . . It was the worst of times

My wattle and daub
(And I don't mean my second chin)

The hedge witch inspired
me to draw this

Drawn
AND
Quartered

Don't throw me
on the cart . . .

The world
according to me

. . . I'm just having a Monday

Stuff to do before the pustules burst:

- ☐ ....
- ☐ ....
- ☐ ....
- ☐ ....
- ☐ ....
- ☐ ....
- ☐ ....
- ☐ ....
- ☐ ....
- ☐ ....
- ☐ ....
- ☐ ....
- ☐ ....
- ☐ ....
- ☐ ....
- ☐ ....

Emotional check~in
(How is your plague?)

	The rash is gone!	Slightly flushed	A few pustules	Throw me on the cart
S	◯	◯	◯	◯
M	◯	◯	◯	◯
T	◯	◯	◯	◯
W	◯	◯	◯	◯
T	◯	◯	◯	◯
F	◯	◯	◯	◯
S	◯	◯	◯	◯

Ball~pit of my mind
(dump whatever you want in this space; just wash your hands afterward)

Habit check~in

S	M	T	W	T	F	S
◯	◯	◯	◯	◯	◯	◯
◯	◯	◯	◯	◯	◯	◯
◯	◯	◯	◯	◯	◯	◯
◯	◯	◯	◯	◯	◯	◯
◯	◯	◯	◯	◯	◯	◯
◯	◯	◯	◯	◯	◯	◯
◯	◯	◯	◯	◯	◯	◯

(Did you do your stuff?)

Turning lead into gold.

J·F·M·A·M·J·J·A·S·O·N·D

_____,

_____ week of the plague

Fair winds or foul?

Feeding the huddled masses

1

2

3

4

It was the best of times . . .

. . . It was the worst of times

My wattle and daub
(And I don't mean my second chin)

The hedge witch inspired
me to draw this

Don't throw me
on the cart . . .

Drawn
AND
Quartered

The world
according to me

. . . I'm just having a Monday

Stuff to do before the pustules burst:

- [ ]
- [ ]
- [ ]
- [ ]
- [ ]
- [ ]
- [ ]
- [ ]
- [ ]
- [ ]
- [ ]
- [ ]
- [ ]
- [ ]
- [ ]
- [ ]
- [ ]
- [ ]

Emotional check~in
(How is your plague?)

	The rash is gone!	Slightly flushed	A few pustules	Throw me on the cart
S	○	○	○	○
M	○	○	○	○
T	○	○	○	○
W	○	○	○	○
T	○	○	○	○
F	○	○	○	○
S	○	○	○	○

Ball~pit of my mind
(dump whatever you want in this space; just wash your hands afterward)

Habit check~in

S	M	T	W	T	F	S
○	○	○	○	○	○	○
○	○	○	○	○	○	○
○	○	○	○	○	○	○
○	○	○	○	○	○	○
○	○	○	○	○	○	○
○	○	○	○	○	○	○
○	○	○	○	○	○	○

(Did you do your stuff?)

Today, fate is being . . .

J·F·M·A·M·J·J·A·S·O·N·D

_____ ,

_____ week of the plague

Fair winds or foul?

It was the best of times . . .

. . . It was the worst of times

Feeding the huddled masses

                  1

2

                  3

4

My wattle and daub
(And I don't mean my second chin)

The hedge witch inspired
me to draw this

Don't throw me
on the cart . . .

Drawn
AND
Quartered

The world
according to me

. . . I'm just having a Monday

Stuff to do before the pustules burst:

- ☐
- ☐
- ☐
- ☐
- ☐
- ☐
- ☐
- ☐
- ☐
- ☐
- ☐
- ☐
- ☐
- ☐
- ☐
- ☐
- ☐
- ☐

Emotional check~in
(How is your plague?)

	The rash is gone!	Slightly flushed	A few pustules	Throw me on the cart
S	○	○	○	○
M	○	○	○	○
T	○	○	○	○
W	○	○	○	○
T	○	○	○	○
F	○	○	○	○
S	○	○	○	○

Ball~pit of my mind
(dump whatever you want in this space; just wash your hands afterward)

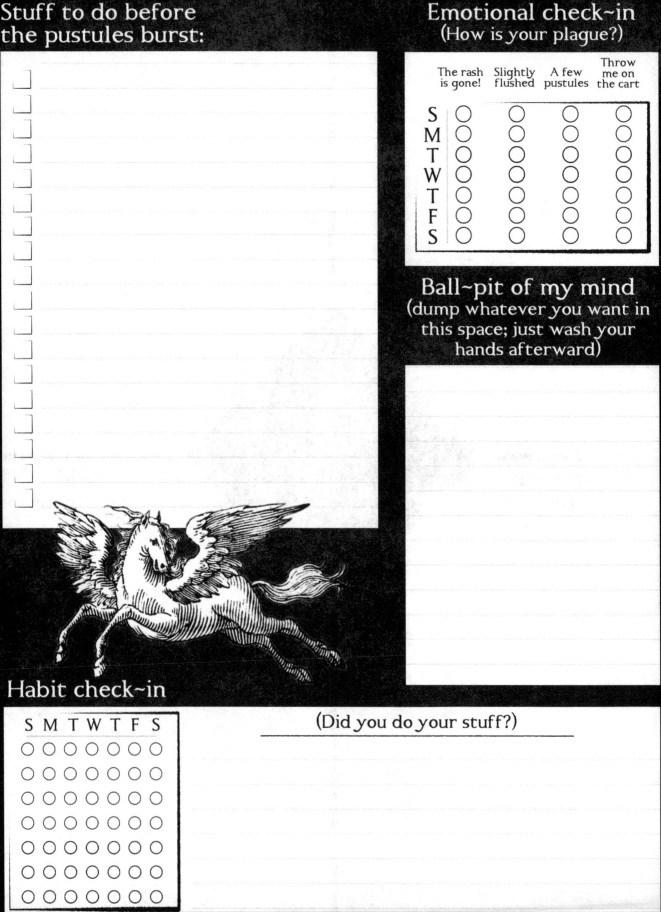

Habit check~in

S	M	T	W	T	F	S
○	○	○	○	○	○	○
○	○	○	○	○	○	○
○	○	○	○	○	○	○
○	○	○	○	○	○	○
○	○	○	○	○	○	○
○	○	○	○	○	○	○
○	○	○	○	○	○	○

(Did you do your stuff?)

The Oracle says . . .

J·F·M·A·M·J·J·A·S·O·N·D

_____ ,

_____ week of the plague

Fair winds or foul?

Feeding the huddled masses

1

2

3

4

It was the best of times . . .

. . . It was the worst of times

My wattle and daub
(And I don't mean my second chin)

The hedge witch inspired
me to draw this

Don't throw me
on the cart . . .

Drawn
AND
Quartered

The world
according to me

. . . I'm just having a Monday

Stuff to do before the pustules burst:

- ☐
- ☐
- ☐
- ☐
- ☐
- ☐
- ☐
- ☐
- ☐
- ☐
- ☐
- ☐
- ☐
- ☐
- ☐
- ☐
- ☐
- ☐
- ☐

Emotional check~in
(How is your plague?)

	The rash is gone!	Slightly flushed	A few pustules	Throw me on the cart
S	○	○	○	○
M	○	○	○	○
T	○	○	○	○
W	○	○	○	○
T	○	○	○	○
F	○	○	○	○
S	○	○	○	○

Ball~pit of my mind
(dump whatever you want in this space; just wash your hands afterward)

Habit check~in

S	M	T	W	T	F	S
○	○	○	○	○	○	○
○	○	○	○	○	○	○
○	○	○	○	○	○	○
○	○	○	○	○	○	○
○	○	○	○	○	○	○
○	○	○	○	○	○	○
○	○	○	○	○	○	○

(Did you do your stuff?)

Aligning my humours . . .

J·F·M·A·M·J·J·A·S·O·N·D

_____,

_____ week of the plague

Fair winds or foul?

Feeding the huddled masses

1

2

3

4

It was the best of times . . .

. . . It was the worst of times

My wattle and daub
(And I don't mean my second chin)

The hedge witch inspired
me to draw this

Drawn
AND
Quartered

Don't throw me
on the cart . . .

The world
according to me

. . . I'm just having a Monday

Stuff to do before the pustules burst:

- [ ]
- [ ]
- [ ]
- [ ]
- [ ]
- [ ]
- [ ]
- [ ]
- [ ]
- [ ]
- [ ]
- [ ]
- [ ]
- [ ]
- [ ]
- [ ]
- [ ]
- [ ]
- [ ]

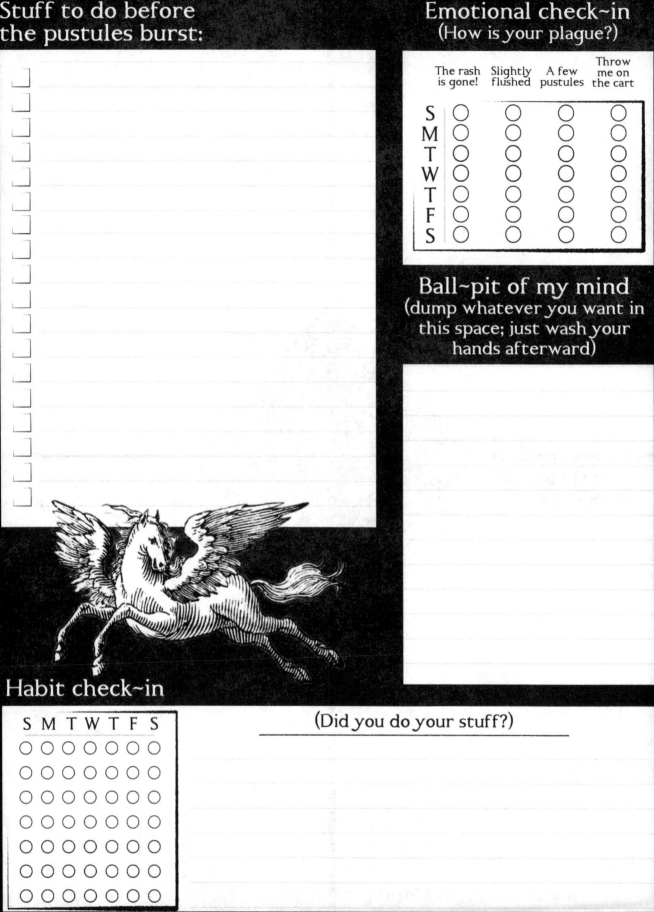

Emotional check~in
(How is your plague?)

	The rash is gone!	Slightly flushed	A few pustules	Throw me on the cart
S	○	○	○	○
M	○	○	○	○
T	○	○	○	○
W	○	○	○	○
T	○	○	○	○
F	○	○	○	○
S	○	○	○	○

Ball~pit of my mind
(dump whatever you want in this space; just wash your hands afterward)

Habit check~in

S	M	T	W	T	F	S
○	○	○	○	○	○	○
○	○	○	○	○	○	○
○	○	○	○	○	○	○
○	○	○	○	○	○	○
○	○	○	○	○	○	○
○	○	○	○	○	○	○
○	○	○	○	○	○	○

(Did you do your stuff?)

It's written in the stars.

J·F·M·A·M·J·J·A·S·O·N·D

_____,

_____ week of the plague

Fair winds or foul?

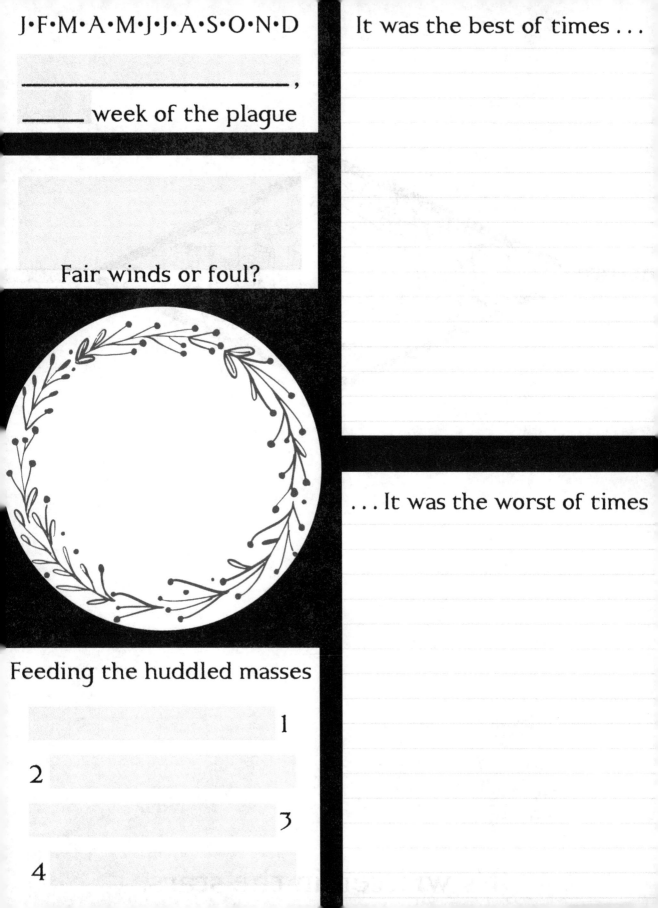

Feeding the huddled masses

1

2

3

4

It was the best of times . . .

. . . It was the worst of times

My wattle and daub
(And I don't mean my second chin)

The hedge witch inspired
me to draw this

Drawn AND Quartered

Don't throw me
on the cart . . .

The world
according to me

. . . I'm just having a Monday

Stuff to do before the pustules burst:

- ☐
- ☐
- ☐
- ☐
- ☐
- ☐
- ☐
- ☐
- ☐
- ☐
- ☐
- ☐
- ☐
- ☐
- ☐
- ☐
- ☐
- ☐

Emotional check~in
(How is your plague?)

	The rash is gone!	Slightly flushed	A few pustules	Throw me on the cart
S	○	○	○	○
M	○	○	○	○
T	○	○	○	○
W	○	○	○	○
T	○	○	○	○
F	○	○	○	○
S	○	○	○	○

Ball~pit of my mind
(dump whatever you want in this space; just wash your hands afterward)

Habit check~in

S	M	T	W	T	F	S
○	○	○	○	○	○	○
○	○	○	○	○	○	○
○	○	○	○	○	○	○
○	○	○	○	○	○	○
○	○	○	○	○	○	○
○	○	○	○	○	○	○
○	○	○	○	○	○	○

(Did you do your stuff?)

Love in the time of the plague.

J·F·M·A·M·J·J·A·S·O·N·D

_____,

_____ week of the plague

Fair winds or foul?

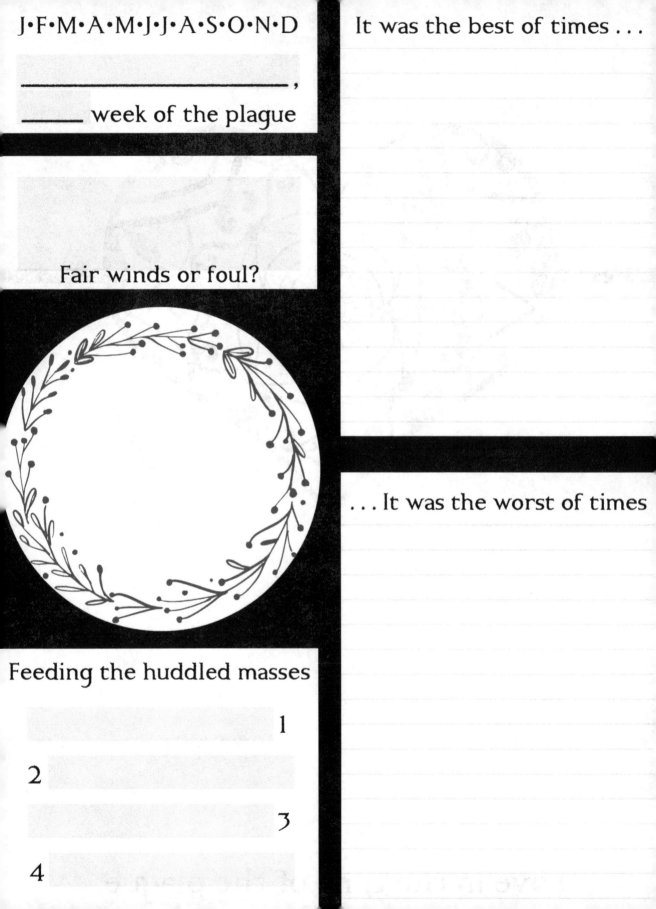

It was the best of times . . .

. . . It was the worst of times

Feeding the huddled masses

1

2

3

4

My wattle and daub
(And I don't mean my second chin)

The hedge witch inspired
me to draw this

Drawn AND Quartered

Don't throw me
on the cart . . .

The world
according to me

. . . I'm just having a Monday

Stuff to do before the pustules burst:

- [ ]
- [ ]
- [ ]
- [ ]
- [ ]
- [ ]
- [ ]
- [ ]
- [ ]
- [ ]
- [ ]
- [ ]
- [ ]
- [ ]
- [ ]
- [ ]
- [ ]
- [ ]

Emotional check~in
(How is your plague?)

	The rash is gone!	Slightly flushed	A few pustules	Throw me on the cart
S	○	○	○	○
M	○	○	○	○
T	○	○	○	○
W	○	○	○	○
T	○	○	○	○
F	○	○	○	○
S	○	○	○	○

Ball~pit of my mind
(dump whatever you want in this space; just wash your hands afterward)

Habit check~in

S	M	T	W	T	F	S
○	○	○	○	○	○	○
○	○	○	○	○	○	○
○	○	○	○	○	○	○
○	○	○	○	○	○	○
○	○	○	○	○	○	○
○	○	○	○	○	○	○
○	○	○	○	○	○	○

(Did you do your stuff?)

Turning lead into gold.

J·F·M·A·M·J·J·A·S·O·N·D

_____ ,

_____ week of the plague

Fair winds or foul?

Feeding the huddled masses

1

2

3

4

It was the best of times . . .

. . . It was the worst of times

My wattle and daub
(And I don't mean my second chin)

The hedge witch inspired
me to draw this

Drawn
AND
Quartered

Don't throw me
on the cart . . .

The world
according to me

. . . I'm just having a Monday

Stuff to do before the pustules burst:

- ☐
- ☐
- ☐
- ☐
- ☐
- ☐
- ☐
- ☐
- ☐
- ☐
- ☐
- ☐
- ☐
- ☐
- ☐
- ☐
- ☐

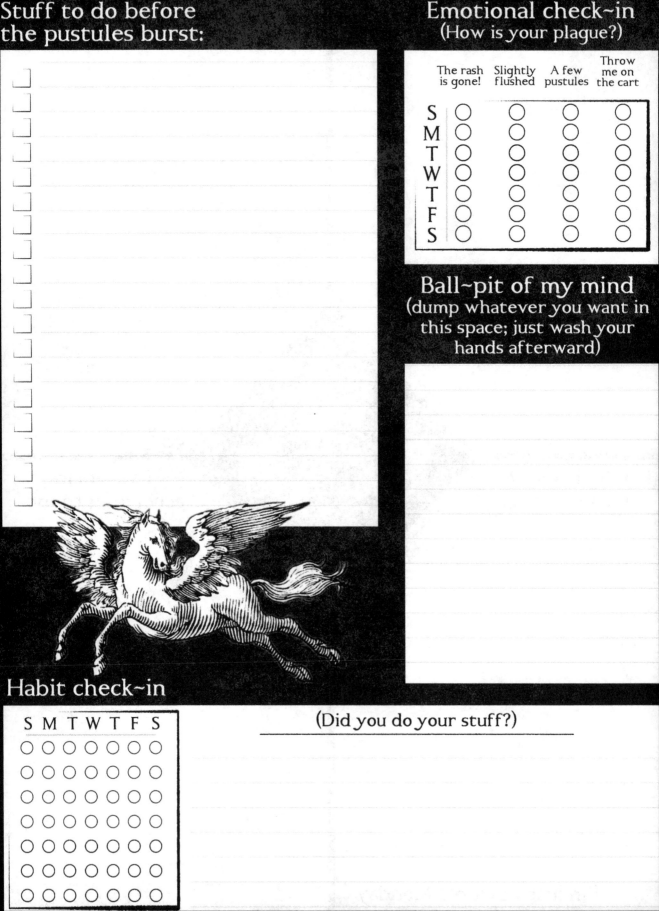

Emotional check~in
(How is your plague?)

	The rash is gone!	Slightly flushed	A few pustules	Throw me on the cart
S	○	○	○	○
M	○	○	○	○
T	○	○	○	○
W	○	○	○	○
T	○	○	○	○
F	○	○	○	○
S	○	○	○	○

Ball~pit of my mind
(dump whatever you want in this space; just wash your hands afterward)

Habit check~in

S	M	T	W	T	F	S
○	○	○	○	○	○	○
○	○	○	○	○	○	○
○	○	○	○	○	○	○
○	○	○	○	○	○	○
○	○	○	○	○	○	○
○	○	○	○	○	○	○
○	○	○	○	○	○	○

(Did you do your stuff?)

Today, fate is being . . .

J·F·M·A·M·J·J·A·S·O·N·D

_____,

_____ week of the plague

It was the best of times . . .

Fair winds or foul?

. . . It was the worst of times

Feeding the huddled masses

1

2

3

4

My wattle and daub
(And I don't mean my second chin)

The hedge witch inspired
me to draw this

Drawn
AND
Quartered

Don't throw me
on the cart . . .

The world
according to me

. . . I'm just having a Monday

the pustules burst:

- [ ]
- [ ]
- [ ]
- [ ]
- [ ]
- [ ]
- [ ]
- [ ]
- [ ]
- [ ]
- [ ]
- [ ]
- [ ]
- [ ]
- [ ]
- [ ]
- [ ]
- [ ]

(How is your plague?)

	The rash is gone!	Slightly flushed	A few pustules	Throw me on the cart
S	○	○	○	○
M	○	○	○	○
T	○	○	○	○
W	○	○	○	○
T	○	○	○	○
F	○	○	○	○
S	○	○	○	○

Ball~pit of my mind
(dump whatever you want in this space; just wash your hands afterward)

Habit check~in

S	M	T	W	T	F	S
○	○	○	○	○	○	○
○	○	○	○	○	○	○
○	○	○	○	○	○	○
○	○	○	○	○	○	○
○	○	○	○	○	○	○
○	○	○	○	○	○	○
○	○	○	○	○	○	○

(Did you do your stuff?)

The Oracle says . . .

Content of an indeterminate nature.

Content of an indeterminate nature.

Content of an indeterminate nature.

Content of an indeterminate nature.

Content of an indeterminate nature.

Content of an indeterminate nature.

Content of an indeterminate nature.

Content of an indeterminate nature.

Content of an indeterminate nature.

Content of an indeterminate nature.

Content of an indeterminate nature.

Content of an indeterminate nature.

Content of an indeterminate nature.

Content of an indeterminate nature.

Content of an indeterminate nature.

Content of an indeterminate nature.

Content of an indeterminate nature.

Content of an indeterminate nature.

PEN TEST PAGE
Test your media here (pens, pencils, paint, markers, etc.)

PEN TEST PAGE

Test your media here (pens, pencils, paint, markers, etc.)

NOTE TO READERS

My lovely one! We hope you enjoyed playing with this journal, which we handcrafted from the finest artisanal words and graphics just for you.

If you are one of the folks who likes to review books, we'd love it if you posted a review for it on your favorite book spot. If you aren't a reviewing type, fear not, we will cherish you regardless.

We'd also like to encourage you to sign up for our newsletter at www.subscribepage.com/u5l9j8. Feel free to send/share with us any of your fun journal entries (but don't post anything you don't want everyone to see, or which would offend small children and dogs). You can share with us on our Facebook page at www.facebook.com/bee.moon.75491, or via e-mail at beeandmoonbooks@gmail.com.

Blessings of the plague doctor, and don't get on the cart!

*Katie &
L K*